higher-level thinking
Questions
Chemistry

questions by
Angela Manzi
Michael Michels

created and designed by
Miguel Kagan

layout by
Cathy Nguyen

illustrated by
Erin Kant and
Celso Rodriguez

Kagan

Kagan Publishing

981 Calle Amanecer

San Clemente, CA 92673

(949) 545-6300

1 (800) 933-2667

www.KaganOnline.com

ISBN: 978-1-933445-01-4

Table of ❓ Contents

"I had six
honest serving men
They taught me all I knew:
Their names were Where
and What and When
and Why and How
and Who."

— Rudyard Kipling

Introduction

In your hands you hold a powerful book. It is a member of a series of transformative blackline activity books. Between the covers, you will find questions, questions, and more questions! But these are no ordinary questions. These are the important kind—higher-level thinking questions—the kind that stretch your students' minds; the kind that release your students' natural curiosity about the world; the kind that rack your students' brains; the kind that instill in your students a sense of wonderment about your curriculum.

But we are getting a bit ahead of ourselves. Let's start from the beginning. Since this is a book of questions, it seems only appropriate for this introduction to pose a few questions—about the book and its underlying educational philosophy. So Mr. Kipling's Six Honest Serving Men, if you will, please lead the way:

What?
What are higher-level thinking questions?

This is a loaded question (as should be all good questions). Using our analytic thinking skills, let's break this question down into two smaller questions: 1) What is higher-level thinking? and 2) What are questions? When we understand the types of thinking skills and the types of questions, we can combine the best of both worlds, crafting beautiful questions to generate the range of higher-level thinking in our students!

Types of Thinking

There are many different types of thinking. Some types of thinking include:

- applying
- associating
- comparing
- contrasting
- defining
- elaborating
- empathizing
- experimenting
- generalizing
- investigating
- making analogies
- planning
- prioritizing
- recalling
- reflecting
- reversing
- sequencing
- summarizing
- synthesizing
- assessing
- augmenting
- connecting
- decision-making
- drawing conclusions
- eliminating
- evaluating
- explaining
- inferring consequences
- inventing
- memorizing
- predicting
- problem-solving
- reducing
- relating
- role-taking
- substituting
- symbolizing
- understanding
- thinking about thinking (metacognition)

This is quite a formidable list. It's nowhere near complete. Thinking is a big, multifaceted phenomenon. Perhaps the most widely recognized system for classifying thinking and classroom questions is Benjamin Bloom's Taxonomy of Thinking Skills. Bloom's Taxonomy classifies thinking skills into six hierarchical levels. It begins with the lower levels of thinking skills and moves up to higher-level thinking skills: 1) Knowledge, 2) Comprehension, 3) Application, 4) Analysis, 5) Synthesis, 6) Evaluation. See Bloom's Taxonomy on the following page.

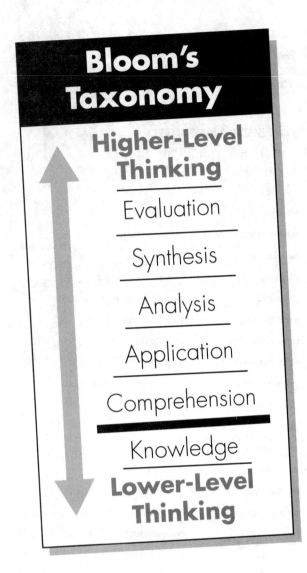

Bloom's Taxonomy

Higher-Level Thinking

Evaluation

Synthesis

Analysis

Application

Comprehension

Knowledge

Lower-Level Thinking

In education, the term "higher-level thinking" often refers to the higher levels of Mr. Bloom's taxonomy. But Bloom's Taxonomy is but one way of organizing and conceptualizing the various types of thinking skills.

There are many ways we can cut the thinking skills pie. We can alternatively view the many different types of thinking skills as, well…many different skills. Some thinking skills may be hierarchical. Some may be interrelated. And some may be relatively independent.

In this book, we take a pragmatic, functional approach. Each type of thinking skill serves a different function. So called "lower-level" thinking skills are very useful for certain purposes. Memorizing and understanding information

are invaluable skills that our students will use throughout their lives. But so too are many of the "higher-level" thinking skills on our list. The more facets of students' thinking skills we develop, the better we prepare them for lifelong success.

Because so much classroom learning heretofore has focused on the "lower rungs" of the thinking skills ladder—knowledge and comprehension, or memorization and understanding—in this series of books we have chosen to focus on questions to generate "higher-level" thinking. This book is an attempt to correct the imbalance in the types of thinking skills developed by classroom questions.

Types of Questions

As we ask questions of our students, we further promote cognitive development when we use Fat questions, Low-Consensus questions, and True questions.

Fat Questions vs. Skinny Questions

Skinny questions are questions that require a skinny answer. For example, after reading a poem, we can ask: "Did you like the poem?" Even though this question could be categorized as an Evaluation question—Bloom's highest level of thinking— it can be answered with one monosyllabic word: "Yes" or "No." How much thinking are we actually generating in our students?

We can reframe this question to make it a fat question: "What things did you like about the poem? What things did you dislike?" Notice no short answer will do. Answering this fattened-up question requires more elaboration. These fat questions presuppose not that there is only one thing but things plural that the student liked and things that she did not like. Making things plural is one way to make skinny questions fat. Students stretch their minds to come up with multiple ideas or solutions. Other easy ways to make questions fat is to add "Why or why not?" or "Explain" or "Describe" or "Defend your position" to the end of a question. These additions promote elaboration beyond a skinny answer. Because language and thought are intimately intertwined, questions that require elaborate responses stretch students' thinking: They grapple to articulate their thoughts.

The type of questions we ask impact not just the type of thinking we develop in our students, but also the depth of thought. Fat questions elicit fat responses. Fat responses develop both depth of thinking and range of thinking skills. The questions in this book are designed to elicit fat responses—deep and varied thinking.

High-Consensus Questions vs. Low-Consensus Questions

A high-consensus question is one to which most people would give the same response, usually a right or wrong answer. After learning about sound, we can ask our students: "What is the name of a room specially designed to improve acoustics for the audience?" This is a high-consensus question. The answer (auditorium) is either correct or incorrect.

Compare the previous question with a low-consensus question: "If you were going to build an auditorium, what special design features would you take into consideration?" Notice, to the low-consensus question there is no right or wrong answer. Each person formulates his or her unique response. To answer, students must apply what they learned, use their ingenuity and creativity.

High-consensus questions promote convergent thinking. With high-consensus questions we strive to direct students *what to think*. Low-consensus questions promote divergent thinking, both critical and creative. With low-consensus

questions we strive to develop students' *ability to think*. The questions in this book are low-consensus questions designed to promote independent, critical and creative thought.

True Questions vs. Review Questions

We all know what review questions are. They're the ones in the back of every chapter and unit. Review questions ask students to regurgitate previously stated or learned information. For example, after learning about the rain forest we may ask: "What percent of the world's oxygen does the rain forest produce?" Students can go back a few pages in their books or into their memory banks and pull out the answer. This is great if we are working on memorization skills, but does little to develop "higher-order" thinking skills.

True questions, on the other hand, are meaningful questions—questions to which we do not know the answer. For example: "What might happen if all the world's rain forests were cut down?" This is a hypothetical; we don't know the answer but considering the question forces us to think. We infer some logical consequences based on what we know. The goal of true questions is not a correct answer, but the thinking journey students take to create a meaningful response. True questions are more representative of real life. Seldom is there a black and white answer. In life, we struggle with ambiguity, confounding variables, and uncertain outcomes. There are millions of shades of gray. True questions prepare students to deal with life's uncertainties.

When we ask a review question, we know the answer and are checking to see if the student does also. When we ask a true question, it is truly a question. We don't necessarily know the answer and neither does the student. True questions are

> **Education is not the filling of a pail, but the lighting of a fire.**
> — William Butler Yeats

Types of Questions

Skinny →	Fat
• Short Answer	• Elaborated Answer
• Shallow Thinking	• Deep Thinking

High-Consensus →	Low-Consensus
• Right or Wrong Answer	• No Single Correct Answer
• Develops Convergent Thinking	• Develops Divergent Thinking
• "What" to Think	• "How" to Think

Review →	True
• Asker Knows Answer	• Asker Doesn't Know Answer
• Checking for Correctness	• Invitation to Think

often an invitation to think, ponder, speculate, and engage in a questioning process.

We can use true questions in the classroom to make our curriculum more personally meaningful, to promote investigation, and awaken students' sense of awe and wonderment in what we teach. Many questions you will find in this book are true questions designed to make the content provocative, intriguing, and personally relevant.

The box above summarizes the different types of questions. The questions you will find in this book are a move away from skinny, high-consensus, review questions toward fat, low-consensus true questions. As we ask these types of questions in our class, we transform even mundane content into a springboard for higher-level thinking. As we integrate these question gems into our daily lessons, we create powerful learning experiences. ***We do not fill our students' pails with knowledge; we kindle their fires to become lifetime thinkers.***

Why?
Why should I use higher-level thinking questions in my classroom?

Major shifts in our economic structure are changing the ways we work and live. The direction is increasingly toward an information-based, high-tech economy. The sum of our technological information is exploding. We could give you a figure how rapidly information is doubling, but by the time you read this, the number would be outdated! No kidding.

But this is no surprise. This is our daily reality. We see it around us everyday and on the news: cloning, gene manipulation, e-mail, the Internet, Mars rovers, electric cars, hybrids, laser surgery, CD-ROMs, DVDs. All around us we see the wheels of progress turning: New discoveries, new technologies, a new societal knowledge and information base. New jobs are being created today in fields that simply didn't exist yesterday.

How do we best prepare our students for this uncertain future—a future in which the only constant will be change? As we are propelled into a world of ever-increasing change, what is the relative value of teaching students facts versus thinking skills? This point becomes even more salient when we realize that students cannot master everything, and many facts will soon become obsolete. Facts become outdated or irrelevant. Thinking skills are for a lifetime. Increasingly, how we define educational success will be away from the quantity of information mastered. Instead, we will define success as our students' ability to generate questions, apply, synthesize, predict, evaluate, compare, categorize.

If we as professionals are to proactively respond to these societal shifts, thinking skills will become central to our curriculum. Whether we teach thinking skills directly, or we integrate them into our curriculum, the power to think is the greatest gift we can give our students!

We believe the questions you will find in this book are a step in the direction of preparing students for lifelong success. The goal is to develop independent thinkers who are critical and creative, regardless of the content. We hope the books in this series are more than sets of questions. We provide them as a model approach to questioning in the classroom.

On pages 8 and 9, you will find Questions to Engage Students' Thinking Skills. These pages contain numerous types of thinking and questions designed to engage each thinking skill. As you make your own questions for your students with your own content, use these question starters to help you frame your questions to stimulate various facets of your students' thinking skills. Also let your students

> **Virtually the only predictable trend is continuing change.**
>
> — Dr. Linda Tsantis,
> Creating the Future

use these question starters to generate their own higher-level thinking questions about the curriculum.

Who?
Who is this book for?

This book is for you and your students, but mostly for your students. It is designed to help make your job easier. Inside you will find hundreds of ready-to-use reproducible questions. Sometimes in the press for time we opt for what is easy over what is best. These books attempt to make easy what is best. In this treasure chest, you will find hours and hours of timesaving ready-made questions and activities.

Place Higher-Level Thinking In Your Students' Hands

As previously mentioned, this book is even more for your students than for you. As teachers, we ask a tremendous number of questions. Primary teachers ask 3.5 to 6.5 questions per minute! Elementary teachers average 348 questions a day. How many questions would you predict our students ask? Researchers asked this question. What they found was shocking: Typical students ask approximately one question per month.* One question per month!

Although this study may not be representative of your classroom, it does suggest that in general, as teachers we are missing out on a very powerful force—student-generated questions.

---

* Myra & David Sadker, "Questioning Skills" in *Classroom Teaching Skills*, 2nd ed. Lexington, MA: D.C. Heath & Co., 1982.

Questions to Engage Students' Thinking Skills

Analyzing
• How could you break down…?
• What components…?
• What qualities/characteristics…?

Applying
• How is _____ an example of…?
• What practical applications…?
• What examples…?
• How could you use…?
• How does this apply to…?
• In your life, how would you apply…?

Assessing
• By what criteria would you assess…?
• What grade would you give…?
• How could you improve…?

Augmenting/Elaborating
• What ideas might you add to…?
• What more can you say about…?

Categorizing/Classifying/Organizing
• How might you classify…?
• If you were going to categorize…?

Comparing/Contrasting
• How would you compare…?
• What similarities…?
• What are the differences between…?
• How is _____ different…?

Connecting/Associating
• What do you already know about…?
• What connections can you make between…?
• What things do you think of when you think of…?

Decision-Making
• How would you decide…?
• If you had to choose between…?

Defining
• How would you define…?
• In your own words, what is…?

Describing/Summarizing
• How could you describe/summarize…?
• If you were a reporter, how would you describe…?

Determining Cause/Effect
• What is the cause of…?
• How does _____ effect _____?
• What impact might…?

Drawing Conclusions/ Inferring Consequences
• What conclusions can you draw from…?
• What would happen if…?
• What would have happened if…?
• If you changed _____, what might happen?

Eliminating
• What part of _____ might you eliminate?
• How could you get rid of…?

Evaluating
• What is your opinion about…?
• Do you prefer…?
• Would you rather…?
• What is your favorite…?
• Do you agree or disagree…?
• What are the positive and negative aspects of…?
• What are the advantages and disadvantages…?
• If you were a judge…?
• On a scale of 1 to 10, how would you rate…?
• What is the most important…?
• Is it better or worse…?

Explaining
• How can you explain…?
• What factors might explain…?

Higher-Level Thinking Questions for Chemistry
Kagan Publishing • 1 (800) 933-2667 • www.KaganOnline.com

Experimenting
- How could you test...?
- What experiment could you do to...?

Generalizing
- What general rule can...?
- What principle could you apply...?
- What can you say about all...?

Interpreting
- Why is _____ important?
- What is the significance of...?
- What role...?
- What is the moral of...?

Inventing
- What could you invent to...?
- What machine could...?

Investigating
- How could you find out more about...?
- If you wanted to know about...?

Making Analogies
- How is _____ like _____?
- What analogy can you invent for...?

Observing
- What observations did you make about...?
- What changes...?

Patterning
- What patterns can you find...?
- How would you describe the organization of...?

Planning
- What preparations would you...?

Predicting/Hypothesizing
- What would you predict...?
- What is your theory about...?
- If you were going to guess...?

Prioritizing
- What is more important...?
- How might you prioritize...?

Problem-Solving
- How would you approach the problem?
- What are some possible solutions to...?

Reducing/Simplifying
- In a word, how would you describe...?
- How can you simplify...?

Reflecting/Metacognition
- What would you think if...?
- How can you describe what you were thinking when...?

Relating
- How is _____ related to _____?
- What is the relationship between...?
- How does _____ depend on _____?

Reversing/Inversing
- What is the opposite of...?

Role-Taking/Empathizing
- If you were (someone/something else)...?
- How would you feel if...?

Sequencing
- How could you sequence...?
- What steps are involved in...?

Substituting
- What could have been used instead of...?
- What else could you use for...?
- What might you substitute for...?
- What is another way...?

Symbolizing
- How could you draw...?
- What symbol best represents...?

Synthesizing
- How could you combine...?
- What could you put together...?

The capacity to answer higher-level thinking questions is a wonderful skill we can give our students, as is the skill to solve problems. Arguably more important skills are the ability to find problems to solve and formulate questions to answer. If we look at the great thinkers of the world—the Einsteins, the Edisons, the Freuds—their thinking is marked by a yearning to solve tremendous questions and problems. It is this questioning process that distinguishes those who illuminate and create our world from those who merely accept it.

> **Asking a good question requires students to think harder than giving a good answer.**
> — Robert Fisher, Teaching Children to Learn

Reflect on this analogy: If we wanted to teach our students to catch and throw, we could bring in one tennis ball and take turns throwing it to each student and having them throw it back to us. Alternatively, we could bring in twenty balls and have our students form small groups and have them toss the ball back and forth to each other. Picture the two classrooms: One with twenty balls being caught at any one moment, and the other with just one. In which class would students better and more quickly learn to catch and throw?

Make Learning an Interactive Process

Higher-level thinking is not just something that occurs between students' ears! Students benefit from an interactive process. This basic premise underlies the majority of activities you will find in this book.

As students discuss questions and listen to others, they are confronted with differing perspectives and are pushed to articulate their own thinking well beyond the level they could attain on their own. Students too have an enormous capacity to mediate each other's learning. When we heterogeneously group students to work together, we create an environment to move students through their zone of proximal development. We also provide opportunities for tutoring and leadership. Verbal interaction with peers in cooperative groups adds a dimension to questions not available with whole-class questions and answers.

The same is true with thinking skills. When we make our students more active participants in the learning process, they are given dramatically more opportunities to produce their own thought and to strengthen their own thinking skills. Would you rather have one question being asked and answered at any one moment in your class, or twenty? Small groups mean more questioning and more thinking. Instead of rarely answering a teacher question or rarely generating their own question, asking and answering questions becomes a regular part of your students' day. It is through cooperative interaction that we truly turn our classroom into a higher-level think tank. The associated personal and social benefits are invaluable.

When?
When do I use higher-level thinking questions?

Do I use these questions at the beginning of the lesson, during the lesson, or after? The answer, of course, is all of the above.

Use these questions or your own thinking questions at the beginning of the lesson to provide a motivational set for the lesson. Pique students' interest about the content with some provocative questions: "What would happen if we didn't have gravity?" "Why did Pilgrims get along with some Native Americans, but not others?" "What do you think this book will be about?" Make the content personally relevant by bringing in students' own knowledge, experiences, and feelings about the content: "What do you know about spiders?" "What things do you like about mystery stories?" "How would you feel if explorers invaded your land and killed your family?" "What do you wonder about electricity?"

Use the higher-level thinking questions throughout your lessons. Use the many questions and activities in this book not as a replacement of your curriculum, but as an additional avenue to explore the content and stretch students' thinking skills.

Use the questions after your lesson. Use the higher-level thinking questions, a journal writing activity, or the question starters as an extension activity to your lesson or unit.

Or just use the questions as stand-alone sponge activities for students or teams who have finished their work and need a challenging project to work on.

It doesn't matter when you use them, just use them frequently. As questioning becomes a habitual part of the classroom day, students' fear of asking silly questions is diminished. As the ancient Chinese proverb states, "Those who ask a silly question may seem a fool for five minutes, but those who do not ask remain a fool for life."

The important thing is to never stop questioning.
— Albert Einstein

As teachers, we should make a conscious effort to ensure that a portion of the many questions we ask on a daily basis are those that move our students beyond rote memorization. When we integrate higher-level thinking questions into our daily lessons, we transform our role from transmitters of knowledge to engineers of learning.

Where?
Where should I keep this book?

Keep it close by. Inside there are 16 sets of questions. Pull it out any time you teach these topics or need a quick, easy, fun activity or journal writing topic.

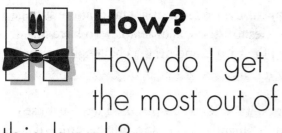

How?
How do I get the most out of this book?

In this book you will find 18 topics arranged alphabetically. For each topic there are reproducible pages for: 1) 16 Question Cards, 2) a Journal Writing activity page, 3) and a Question Starters activity page.

1. Question Cards

The Question Cards are truly the heart of this book. There are numerous ways the Question Cards can be used. After the other activity pages are introduced, you will find a description of a variety of engaging formats to use with the Question Cards.

Specific and General Questions

Some of the questions provided in this book series are content-specific and others are content-free. For example, the literature questions in the Literature books are content-specific. Questions for the *Great Kapok Tree* deal specifically with that literature selection. Some language arts questions in the Language Arts book, on the other hand, are content-free. They are general questions that can be used over and over again with new content. For example, the Book Review questions can be used after reading any book. The Story Structure questions can be used after reading any story. You can tell by glancing at the title of the set and some of the questions whether the set is content-specific or content-free.

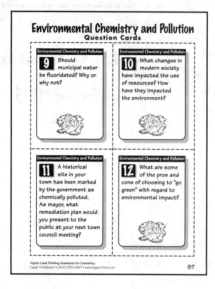

A Little Disclaimer

Not all of the "questions" on the Question Cards are actually questions. Some instruct students to do something. For example, "Compare and contrast…" We can also use these directives to develop the various facets of students' thinking skills.

The Power of Think Time

As you and your students use these questions, don't forget about the power of Think Time! There are two different think times. The first is the time between the question and the response. The second is the time between the response and feedback on the response. Think time has been shown to greatly enhance the quality of student thinking. If students are not pausing for either think time, or doing it too briefly, emphasize its importance. Five little seconds of silent think time after the question and five more seconds before feedback are proven, powerful ways to promote higher-level thinking in your class.

Use Your Question Cards for Years

For attractive Question Cards that will last for years, photocopy them on cardstock and laminate them. To save time, have the Materials Monitor from each team pick up one card set, a pair of scissors for the team, and an envelope or rubber band. Each team cuts out their own set of Question Cards. When they are done with the activity, students can place the Question Cards in the envelope and write the name of the set on the envelope or wrap the cards with a rubber band for storage.

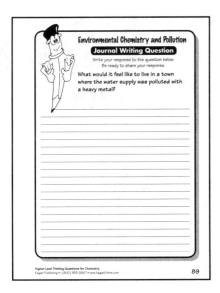

2. Journal Question

The Journal Writing page contains one of the 16 questions as a journal writing prompt. You can substitute any question, or use one of your own. The power of journal writing cannot be overstated. The act of writing takes longer than speaking and thinking. It allows the brain time to make deep connections to the content. Writing requires the writer to present his or her response in clear, concise language. Writing develops both strong thinking and communication skills.

A helpful activity before journal writing is to have students discuss the question in pairs or in small teams. Students discuss their ideas and what they plan to write. This little prewriting activity ignites ideas for those students who stare blankly at their Journal Writing page. The interpersonal interaction further helps students articulate what they are thinking about the topic and invites students to delve deeper into the topic.

Tell students before they write that they will share their journal entries with a partner or with their team. This motivates many students to improve their entry. Sharing written responses also promotes flexible thinking with open-ended questions, and allows students to hear their peers' responses, ideas, and writing styles.

Have students keep a collection of their journal entries in a three-ring binder. This way you can collect them if you wish for assessment or have students go back to reflect on their own learning. If you are using questions across the curriculum, each subject can have its own journal or own section within the binder. Use the provided blackline on the following page for a cover for students' journals or have students design their own.

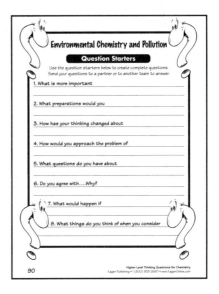

3. Question Starters

The Question Starters activity page is designed to put the questions in the hands of your students. Use these question starters to scaffold your students' ability to write their own thinking questions. This page includes eight question starters to direct students to generate questions across the levels and types of thinking. This Question Starters activity page can be used in a few different ways:

Individual Questions

Have students independently come up with their own questions. When done, they can trade their questions with a partner. On a separate sheet of paper students answer their partners' questions. After answering, partners can share how they answered each other's questions.

JOURNAL

My Best Thinking

This Journal Belongs to _____

Higher-Level Thinking Questions for Chemistry
Kagan Publishing • 1 (800) 933-2667 • www.KaganOnline.com

Pair Questions

Students work in pairs to generate questions to send to another pair. Partners take turns writing each question and also take turns recording each answer. After answering, pairs pair up to share how they answered each other's questions.

Team Questions

Students work in teams to generate questions to send to another team. Teammates take turns writing each question and recording each answer. After answering, teams pair up to share how they answered each other's questions.

Teacher-Led Questions

For young students, lead the whole class in coming up with good higher-level thinking questions.

Teach Your Students About Thinking and Questions

An effective tool to improve students' thinking skills is to teach students about the types of thinking skills and types of questions. Teaching students about the types of thinking skills improves their metacognitive abilities. When students are aware of the types of thinking, they may more effectively plan, monitor, and evaluate their own thinking. When students understand the types of questions and the basics of question construction, they are more likely to create effective higher-level thinking questions. In doing so they develop their own thinking skills and the thinking of classmates as they work to answer each other's questions.

Table of Activities

The Question Cards can be used in a variety of game-like formats to forge students' thinking skills. They can be used for cooperative team and pair work, for whole-class questioning, for independent activities, or at learning centers. On the following pages you will find numerous excellent options to use with your Question Cards. As you use the Question Cards in this book, try the different activities listed below to add novelty and variety to the higher-level thinking process.

Activities

Question Commander

Preferably in teams of four, students shuffle their Question Cards and place them in a stack, questions facing down, so that all teammates can easily reach the Question Cards. Give each team a Question Commander set of instructions (blackline provided on following page) to lead them through each question.

Student One becomes the Question Commander for the first question. The Question Commander reads the question aloud to the team, then asks the teammates to think about the question and how they would answer it. After the think time, the Question Commander selects a teammate to answer the question. The Question Commander may spin a spinner or roll a die to select who will answer. After the teammate gives the answer, Question Commander again calls for think time, this time asking the team to think about the answer. After the think time, the Question Commander leads a team

discussion in which any teammember can contribute his or her thoughts or ideas to the question, or give praise or reactions to the answer.

When the discussion is over, Student Two becomes the Question Commander for the next question.

Question Commander

Question Commander
Instruction Cards

Question Commander

1. Ask the Question: Question Commander reads the question to the team.

2. Think Time: "Think of your best answer."

3. Answer the Question: The Question Commander selects a teammate to answer the question.

4. Think Time: "Think about how you would answer differently or add to the answer."

5. Team Discussion: As a team, discuss other possible answers or reactions to the answer given.

Question Commander

1. Ask the Question: Question Commander reads the question to the team.

2. Think Time: "Think of your best answer."

3. Answer the Question: The Question Commander selects a teammate to answer the question.

4. Think Time: "Think about how you would answer differently or add to the answer."

5. Team Discussion: As a team, discuss other possible answers or reactions to the answer given.

Question Commander

1. Ask the Question: Question Commander reads the question to the team.

2. Think Time: "Think of your best answer."

3. Answer the Question: The Question Commander selects a teammate to answer the question.

4. Think Time: "Think about how you would answer differently or add to the answer."

5. Team Discussion: As a team, discuss other possible answers or reactions to the answer given.

Question Commander

1. Ask the Question: Question Commander reads the question to the team.

2. Think Time: "Think of your best answer."

3. Answer the Question: The Question Commander selects a teammate to answer the question.

4. Think Time: "Think about how you would answer differently or add to the answer."

5. Team Discussion: As a team, discuss other possible answers or reactions to the answer given.

Fan-N-Pick

In a team of four, Student One fans out the question cards, and says, "Pick a card, any card!" Student Two picks a card and reads the question out loud to teammates. After five seconds of think time, Student Three gives his or her answer. After another five seconds of think time, Student Four paraphrases, praises, or adds to the answer given. Students rotate roles for each new round.

Spin-N-Think

Spin-N-Think spinners are available from Kagan to lead teams through the steps of higher-level thinking. Students spin the Spin-N-Think™ spinner to select a student at each stage of the questioning to: 1) ask the question, 2) answer the question, 3) paraphrase and praise the answer, 4) augment the answer, and 5) discuss the question or answer. The Spin-N-Think™ game makes higher-level thinking more fun, and holds students accountable because they are often called upon, but never know when their number will come up.

Three-Step Interview

After the question is read to the team, students pair up. The first step is an interview in which one student interviews the other about the question. In the second step, students remain with their partner but switch roles: The interviewer becomes the interviewee. In the third step, the pairs come back together and each student in turn presents to the team what their partner shared. Three-Step Interview is strong for individual accountability, active listening, and paraphrasing skills.

Team Discussion

Team Discussion is an easy and informal way of processing the questions: Students read a question and then throw it open for discussion. Team Discussion, however, does not ensure that there is individual accountability or equal participation.

Think-Pair-Square

One student reads a question out loud to teammates. Partners on the same side of the table then pair up to discuss the question and their answers. Then, all four students come together for an open discussion about the question.

Question-Write-RoundRobin

Students take turns asking the team the question. After each question is asked, each student writes his or her ideas on a piece of paper. After students have finished writing, in turn they share their ideas. This format creates strong individual accountability because each student is expected to develop and share an answer for every question.

Mix-Pair-Discuss

Each student gets a different Question Card. For 16 to 32 students, use two sets of questions. In this case, it is OK for some students to have the same question. Students get out of their seats and mix around the classroom. They pair up with a partner. One partner reads his or her Question Card and the other answers. Then they switch roles. When done they trade cards and find a new partner. The process is repeated for a predetermined amount of time. The rule is students cannot pair up with the same partner twice. Students may get the same questions twice or more, but each time it is with a new partner. This strategy is a fun, energizing way to ask and answer questions.

Think-Pair-Share

Think-Pair-Share is teacher-directed. The teacher asks the question, then gives students think time. Students then pair up to share their thoughts about the question. After the pair discussion, one student is called on to share with the class what was shared in his or her pair. Think-Pair-Share does not provide as much active participation for students as Think-Pair-Square because only one student is called upon at a time, but is a nice way to do whole-class sharing.

Inside-Outside Circle

Each student gets a Question Card. Half of the students form a circle facing out. The other half forms a circle around the inside circle; each student in the outside circle faces one student in the inside circle. Students in the outside circle ask inside circle students a question. After the inside circle students answer the question, students switch roles questioning and answering. After both have asked and answered a question, they each praise the other's

answers and then hold up a hand indicating they are finished. When most students have a hand up, have students trade cards with their partner and rotate to a new partner. To rotate, tell the outside circle to move to the left. This format is a lively and enjoyable way to ask questions and have students listen to the thinking of many classmates.

Question & Answer

This might sound familiar: Instead of giving students the Question Cards, the teacher asks the questions and calls on one student at a time to answer. This traditional format eliminates simultaneous, cooperative interaction, but may be good for introducing younger students to higher-level questions.

Numbered Heads Together

Students number off in their teams so that every student has a number. The teacher asks a question. Students put their "heads together" to discuss the question. The teacher then calls on a number and selects a student with that number to share what his or her team discussed.

pair activity #1

RallyRobin

Each pair gets a set of Question Cards. Student A in the pair reads the question out loud to his or her partner. Student B answers. Partners take turns asking and answering each question.

Pair Discussion

Partners take turns asking the question. The pair then discusses the answer together. Unlike RallyRobin, students discuss the answer. Both students contribute to answering and to discussing each other's ideas.

Question-Write-Share-Discuss

One partner reads the Question Card out loud to his or her teammate. Both students write down their ideas. Partners take turns sharing what they wrote. Partners discuss how their ideas are similar and different.

Higher-Level Thinking Questions for Chemistry
Kagan Publishing • 1 (800) 933-2667 • www.KaganOnline.com

Journal Writing

Students pick one Question Card and make a journal entry or use the question as the prompt for an essay or creative writing. Have students share their writing with a partner or in turn with teammates.

Independent Answers

Students each get their own set of Questions Cards. Pairs or teams can share a set of questions, or the questions can be written on the board or put on the overhead projector. Students work by themselves to answer the questions on a separate sheet of paper. When done, students can compare their answers with a partner, teammates, or the whole class.

Learning Centers

1. Question Card Center

At one center, have the Question Cards and a Spin-N-Think™ spinner, Question Commander instruction card, or Fan-N-Pick instructions. Students lead themselves through the thinking questions. For individual accountability, have each student record their own answer for each question.

2. Journal Writing Center

At a second center, have a Journal Writing activity page for each student. Students can discuss the question with others at their center, then write their own journal entry. After everyone is done writing, students share what they wrote with other students at their center.

3. Question Starters Center

At a third center, have a Question Starters page. Split the students at the center into two groups. Have both groups create thinking questions using the Question Starters activity page. When the groups are done writing their questions, they trade questions with the other group at their center. When done answering each other's questions, two groups pair up to compare their answers.

Higher-Level Thinking Questions for Chemistry
Kagan Publishing • 1 (800) 933-2667 • www.KaganOnline.com

Acids and Bases

An understanding of the pH scale is crucial for the analysis of chemical reactions involving acids, bases, and salts.

higher-level thinking questions

"Don't bunt.
Aim out of
the ballpark."

— David Ogilvy

Higher-Level Thinking Questions for Chemistry
Kagan Publishing • 1 (800) 933-2667 • www.KaganOnline.com

Acids and Bases
Question Cards

Acids and Bases

1 Why is vinegar commonly used as a cleaner?

Acids and Bases

2 In your own words, what is a neutralization reaction?

Acids and Bases

3 If you had to, would you eliminate acids or bases from the earth? Why?

Acids and Bases

4 How could you explain why acid rain occurs?

Acids and Bases
Question Cards

5 What is common to all buffers?

6 What could you invent to solve the problem of acid rain?

7 Using a drawing, how could you express the addition of vinegar to baking soda?

8 What is the significance of buffers to living organisms?

Acids and Bases
Question Cards

Acids and Bases

9 If you had to be an acid, would you be one with a pH of 2 or a pH of 4? Why?

Acids and Bases

10 What do you predict would happen to an aquatic ecosystem if the pH suddenly became very acidic in nature?

Acids and Bases

11 How are acids used to pickle a cucumber? Describe the chemistry of the process from the viewpoint of the acid.

Acids and Bases

12 Why would it be bad for your digestive system if you used too many antacid tablets?

Acids and Bases
Question Cards

Acids and Bases

13 Lime is often used to neutralize soil that is too acidic. What would happen to the soil and the roots of a plant exposed to a change in pH?

Acids and Bases

14 How are weak acids different from strong acids?

Acids and Bases

15 Design an experiment that could test the effects of adding a base to a buffer.

Acids and Bases

16 How does the equation, Acid + Base = Water + Salt, relate to something in your life? Explain.

Higher-Level Thinking Questions for Chemistry
Kagan Publishing • 1 (800) 933-2667 • www.KaganOnline.com

Acids and Bases

Journal Writing Question

Write your response to the question below.
Be ready to share your response.

What practical applications do acids and bases have in a household?

_____
_____
_____
_____
_____
_____
_____
_____
_____
_____
_____
_____
_____
_____
_____
_____
_____
_____
_____
_____

Acids and Bases

Question Starters

Use the question starters below to create complete questions.
Send your questions to a partner or to another team to answer.

1. If you were an acid

2. Do you think it is possible for bases to

3. Should salts be used

4. What impact might acid rain

5. What would happen if buffers

6. In one sentence, how could bases

7. How is the pH scale like

8. What is another way H+ ions can

Higher-Level Thinking Questions for Chemistry
Kagan Publishing • 1 (800) 933-2667 • www.KaganOnline.com

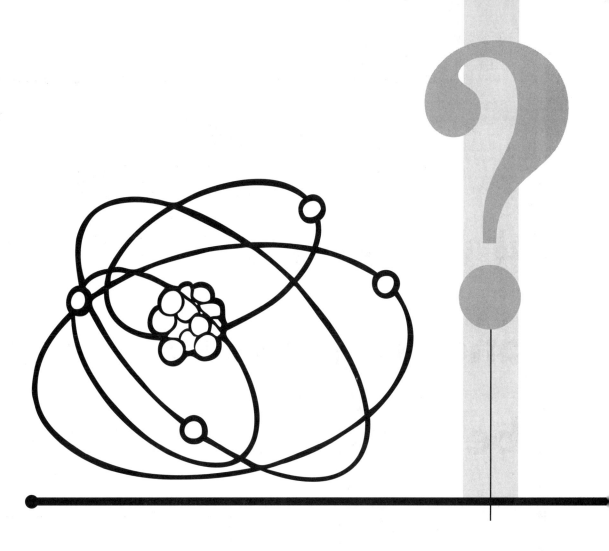

Atomic Structure

The physical makeup of an element's atomic parts, including protons, neutrons, and electrons.

higher-level thinking question

"If I have a thousand ideas and only one turns out to be good, I am satisfied."

— Alfred Bernhard Nobel

Higher-Level Thinking Questions for Chemistry
Kagan Publishing • 1 (800) 933-2667 • www.KaganOnline.com

Atomic Structure

1 How would you define an isotope?

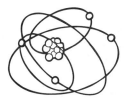

Atomic Structure

2 What is common to the electron configuration of all elements?

Atomic Structure

3 What general rule can be applied to every atom's structure?

Atomic Structure

4 What is the significance of the charges of subatomic particles?

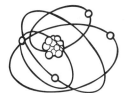

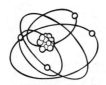

Atomic Structure
Question Cards

Atomic Structure

5 What is another way you could draw an atom?

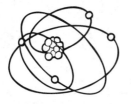

Atomic Structure

6 What connections can you make between electron arrangement and chemical reactivity?

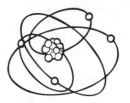

Atomic Structure

7 What role do neutrons play in an atom?

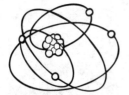

Atomic Structure

8 What are some possible explanations for the arrangement of subatomic particles in an atom?

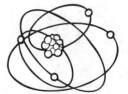

Higher-Level Thinking Questions for Chemistry
Kagan Publishing • 1 (800) 933-2667 • www.KaganOnline.com

Atomic Structure
Question Cards

Atomic Structure

9 Predict what would happen to an atom if the electrons did not travel in orbitals but instead were part of the nuclear mass.

Atomic Structure

10 Describe the travels of an atom's electrons as if you were one of the electrons. What would it feel like?

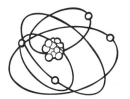

Atomic Structure

11 Compare the structure of an atom to something in life that shows high levels of organization. In what ways are they similar and different?

Atomic Structure

12 How is an atom different from an element?

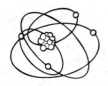

Atomic Structure
Question Cards

Atomic Structure

13 Compare and contrast the characteristics of electrons and protons using a Venn Diagram.

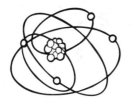

Atomic Structure

14 What are the steps involved in drawing a Lewis Electron Dot Diagram? Draw one for the element of your choice.

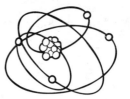

Atomic Structure

15 What patterns can you find in the electron arrangement of the noble gases?

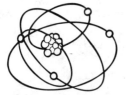

Atomic Structure

16 How can an understanding of isotopes be applied to the real world?

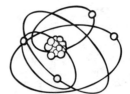

Atomic Structure
Journal Writing Question

Write your response to the question below.
Be ready to share your response.

How would the invention of a new microscope, which can see atoms clearly, revolutionize science?

Atomic Structure

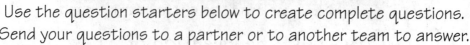
Question Starters

Use the question starters below to create complete questions.
Send your questions to a partner or to another team to answer.

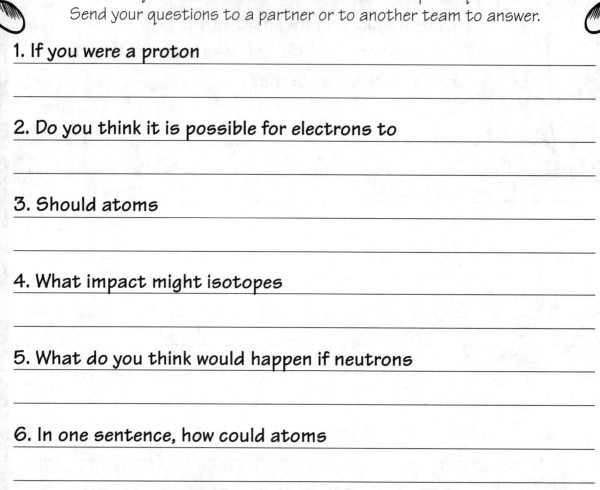

1. If you were a proton

2. Do you think it is possible for electrons to

3. Should atoms

4. What impact might isotopes

5. What do you think would happen if neutrons

6. In one sentence, how could atoms

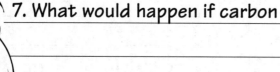

7. What would happen if carbon

8. What is another way atoms can

Higher-Level Thinking Questions for Chemistry
Kagan Publishing • 1 (800) 933-2667 • www.KaganOnline.com

Biochemistry

The study of chemistry involving molecules of biological importance.

higher-level thinking questions

"I believe that every person is born with talent."

— Maya Angelou

Biochemistry
Question Cards

1 What are the similarities and differences between carbohydrates and lipids?

2 In your opinion, what is more important to living things: proteins or nucleic acids? Why?

3 In what order would you rank the following: glucose, starch, cellulose, sucrose, chitin, and glycogen? Why?

4 In your own words, what is ATP and how does it work?

Biochemistry
Question Cards

Biochemistry

5 What role does an enzyme play in a living organism?

Biochemistry

6 What patterns can you find within the structure of biological macromolecules?

Biochemistry

7 How do proteins function in your everyday life?

Biochemistry

8 Compare and contrast the reactions of dehydration synthesis (condensation reaction) and hydrolysis.

Higher-Level Thinking Questions for Chemistry
Kagan Publishing • 1 (800) 933-2667 • www.KaganOnline.com

Biochemistry
Question Cards

Biochemistry

9 If you were stranded on a lifeboat, which would provide you with more energy: a pound of butter or a pound of pasta? Why?

Biochemistry

10 In your own words, define what a polypeptide chain is. How is it similar to a string of beads?

Biochemistry

11 Do you think the government has the right to maintain a DNA bank of every citizen's genetic makeup? Explain.

Biochemistry

12 What are the similarities and differences between the characteristics of an enzyme and an inorganic catalyst?

Biochemistry

13 Two unknown lipids are ready to be used in a recipe at room temperature: one is a solid and the other is a liquid. Which would you use and why?

Biochemistry

14 Compare the energy conversions of photosynthesis and cellular respiration. What are the similarities and differences?

Biochemistry

15 Compare and contrast the chemical properties of fats to carbohydrates, and proteins.

Biochemistry

16 How does a protein's primary structure affect its quaternary structure?

Higher-Level Thinking Questions for Chemistry
Kagan Publishing • 1 (800) 933-2667 • www.KaganOnline.com

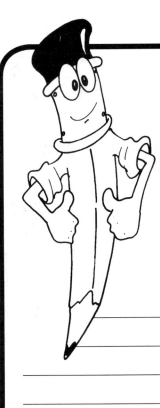

Biochemistry

Journal Writing Question

Write your response to the question below.
Be ready to share your response.

What would you predict would happen to an organism if it ceased to take in lipids?

_____

_____

_____

_____

_____

_____

_____

_____

_____

_____

_____

_____

_____

_____

_____

_____

_____

Biochemistry

Question Starters

Use the question starters below to create complete questions.
Send your questions to a partner or to another team to answer.

1. What if enzymes

2. How could RNA

3. If you were a carbohydrate

4. What general rule

5. In terms of DNA, what is your theory regarding

6. What steps are involved in

 7. What role does a triglyceride play in

8. What could you make

Higher-Level Thinking Questions for Chemistry
Kagan Publishing • 1 (800) 933-2667 • www.KaganOnline.com

Bonding

The forces that hold atoms together within a substance.

higher-level thinking questions

"A single twig breaks, but the bundle of twigs is strong."

— Tecumseh

Higher-Level Thinking Questions for Chemistry
Kagan Publishing • 1 (800) 933-2667 • www.KaganOnline.com

Bonding
Question Cards

Bonding

1 In what ways is a covalent bond like running in a relay race?

Bonding

2 Compare and contrast covalent and ionic bonds.

Bonding

3 Predict which type of bond is stronger: ionic or covalent. Why?

Bonding

4 How could you summarize the steps involved in forming an ionic bond?

Bonding
Question Cards

Bonding

5 What general rule could you develop to determine if an atom will readily form a covalent bond?

Bonding

6 What impact does carbon's diversity in bond formation have on living systems?

Bonding

7 How could you simplify electronegativity?

Bonding

8 What patterns do you observe when forming the covalent bonds during molecule building?

Higher-Level Thinking Questions for Chemistry
Kagan Publishing • 1 (800) 933-2667 • www.KaganOnline.com

Bonding
Question Cards

Bonding

9 What analogy could you create for the process of ionic bonding?

Bonding

10 How could you explain the difference between covalent and polar covalent bonding?

Bonding

11 What would it feel like to be the recipient of an electron in the formation of an ionic bond?

Bonding

12 If you could ask a question about a "lone pair," what would the question be?

Bonding
Question Cards

Bonding

13 How does electronegativity affect a covalent bond?

Bonding

14 In your own words, how would you explain the "octet rule"?

Bonding

15 How could you explain why bond lengths can vary?

Bonding

16 What is the significance of double and triple bonds?

Higher-Level Thinking Questions for Chemistry
Kagan Publishing • 1 (800) 933-2667 • www.KaganOnline.com

Bonding

Journal Writing Question

Write your response to the question below.
Be ready to share your response.

How can you apply your knowledge of bonds in saturated molecules to your diet and health?

_____

_____

_____

_____

_____

_____

_____

_____

_____

_____

_____

_____

_____

_____

_____

_____

_____

Bonding

Question Starters

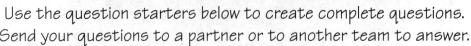
Use the question starters below to create complete questions.
Send your questions to a partner or to another team to answer.

1. How is electronegativity

2. What role do double bonds

3. What is the opposite of

4. What bonding principle could you apply

5. How would you define an electron's

6. In your life, how would you apply

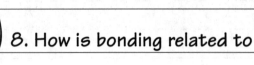
7. What patterns do bonds

8. How is bonding related to

Higher-Level Thinking Questions for Chemistry
Kagan Publishing • 1 (800) 933-2667 • www.KaganOnline.com

Chemical Industry

The use of chemical knowledge in industrial facilities to produce goods and services.

higher-level thinking questions

"The way to get good ideas is to get lots of ideas, and throw the bad ones away."

—— Linus Pauling

Chemical Industry
Question Cards

Chemical Industry

1 How do you think the scent of a flower is converted into a fragrance?

Chemical Industry

2 How could the diffusion of molecules into air affect the daily job of a worker in a chemical plant?

Chemical Industry

3 If you were going to guess, how do you think fertilizers are created and/or tested?

Chemical Industry

4 In what order would you rank the following sweeteners: sugar, sucralose, aspartame, and saccharin? Why?

Chemical Industry
Question Cards

5 What are the pluses and minuses of your school choosing artificial turf grass over real grass for an athletic field?

6 In your own words what is a "generic prescription"?

7 How do you think a jeweler can create different karats of gold?

8 How could you dispose of radioactive soil? Describe at least two different ways.

Chemical Industry
Question Cards

9 What impact might ethanol have on the oil industry?

10 A chemical plant has been trying to build a facility in your town. What questions do you have for the town council, as they debate the proposal?

11 Sequence the steps involved in water treatment, from the source to your tap.

12 What practical applications of chemistry can you identify being used in the field of forensic science?

Chemical Industry
Question Cards

Chemical Industry

13 How does an understanding of atomic particles impact the study of medicine?

Chemical Industry

14 If you could interview a chemist, past or present, what questions would you ask the chemist about his or her career?

Chemical Industry

15 How could you find out more about the uses of chemistry in food science?

Chemical Industry

16 What are the differences between science and technology?

Higher-Level Thinking Questions for Chemistry
Kagan Publishing • 1 (800) 933-2667 • www.KaganOnline.com

Chemical Industry

Journal Writing Question

Write your response to the question below.
Be ready to share your response.

If you were a reporter, how would you describe the hazards of an overturned gasoline truck?

Chemical Industry

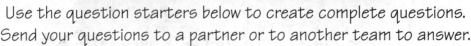
Question Starters

Use the question starters below to create complete questions.
Send your questions to a partner or to another team to answer.

1. How could a flammable liquid _____

_____

2. What could you make using _____

_____

3. How has the creation of plastics _____

_____

4. What could you use instead of glass to _____

_____

5. What are some ways to create _____

_____

6. How could you improve the production of _____

_____

7. What could you invent to _____

_____

8. How would you describe the organization of _____

_____

Higher-Level Thinking Questions for Chemistry
Kagan Publishing • 1 (800) 933-2667 • www.KaganOnline.com

Chemical Reactions

The processes that rearrange substances during a chemical change by breaking and forming bonds.

higher-level thinking questions

"Honest differences are often a healthy sign of progress."

— Mahatma Gandhi

Higher-Level Thinking Questions for Chemistry
Kagan Publishing • 1 (800) 933-2667 • www.KaganOnline.com

Chemical Reactions
Question Cards

Chemical Reactions

1 In your own words, how can you explain the process of balancing a chemical equation?

Chemical Reactions

2 What would it feel like to be a catalyst in action?

Chemical Reactions

3 In your life, how does temperature affect rates of reaction?

Chemical Reactions

4 How is activation energy like an alarm clock going off in the morning?

Chemical Reactions
Question Cards

Chemical Reactions

5 How are enzymes important in the natural world?

Chemical Reactions

6 How is the nitrogen cycle an example of chemical reactions occurring in the real world?

Chemical Reactions

7 What observations can you make about exothermic reactions?

Chemical Reactions

8 How would you compare oxidation and reduction?

Higher-Level Thinking Questions for Chemistry
Kagan Publishing • 1 (800) 933-2667 • www.KaganOnline.com

Chemical Reactions
Question Cards

Chemical Reactions

9 How does an understanding of a precipitation reaction lead to cleaner pipes in a home that has "hard water"?

Chemical Reactions

10 What are the differences between a combustion reaction and a combination reaction?

Chemical Reactions

11 What are the similarities between a displacement reaction and a decomposition reaction?

Chemical Reactions

12 Why do you think an automobile has a catalytic converter in its exhaust system? What would happen if it were removed?

Chemical Reactions
Question Cards

13 In what order would you rank the factors that affect the rate of a chemical reaction? Why?

14 Explain the chemistry involved in galvanic corrosion as it relates to the Statue of Liberty.

15 What are the pros and cons of utilizing nuclear reactions?

16 Why does entropy increase in a chemical system over time? What do you predict would happen if it didn't?

Higher-Level Thinking Questions for Chemistry
Kagan Publishing • 1 (800) 933-2667 • www.KaganOnline.com

Chemical Reactions

Journal Writing Question

Write your response to the question below.
Be ready to share your response.

How is balancing a chemical equation similar to taking inventory in a store?

Chemical Reactions
Question Starters

Use the question starters below to create complete questions.
Send your questions to a partner or to another team to answer.

1. How do endothermic reactions

2. How can reaction rates

3. What impact might catalysts

4. Why does adsorption

5. What could you make using

6. How can activation energy

7. How might you classify

8. What connections can you make between concentration and

Higher-Level Thinking Questions for Chemistry
Kagan Publishing • 1 (800) 933-2667 • www.KaganOnline.com

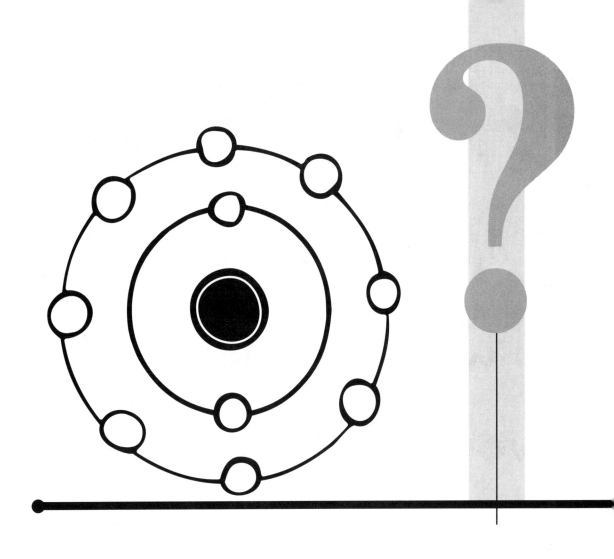

Electron Configurations

The arrangement of electrons around an atom that determine its chemical and physical properties.

higher-level thinking questions

"If we all did the things we are capable of, we would astound ourselves."

— Thomas Edison

Higher-Level Thinking Questions for Chemistry
Kagan Publishing • 1 (800) 933-2667 • www.KaganOnline.com

Electron Configurations
Question Cards

Electron Configurations

1 How is our solar system similar to and different from electrons?

Electron Configurations

2 If you changed one thing about "s" orbitals, what would you change and why?

Electron Configurations

3 How do electron configurations affect reactivity?

Electron Configurations

4 In your own words, how would you describe the organization of electron orbitals?

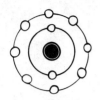

Electron Configurations
Question Cards

5 What are some explanations for electrons grouping themselves in pairs?

6 How do electron configuration patterns in the periodic table impact bonding?

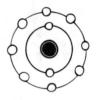

7 What changes occur to electron configurations as the atomic number of an element increases?

8 How has your thinking changed about the noble gases after studying electrons?

Electron Configurations
Question Cards

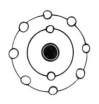

---

9 What do you predict would happen to an atom if its outermost electron shell was full?

---

10 What patterns do you find in the periodic table of elements with regard to electron arrangement?

---

11 What would it feel like to be in an electron shell holding seven electrons versus holding only one electron?

---

12 How is electron configuration similar to stacking objects?

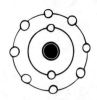

Electron Configurations
Question Cards

Electron Configurations

13 Sketch the electron configuration/molecular geometry of the following:
a. H_2O b. NH_3 c. CH_4

Electron Configurations

14 What analogy can you create to describe electron orbitals?

Electron Configurations

15 Explain what happens to an electron's structure as light is produced during a fireworks display.

Electron Configurations

16 In what ways has the field of medicine changed since the introduction of techniques like MRI (magnetic resonance imaging)? How is a nucleus of an atom similar to a magnet?

Higher-Level Thinking Questions for Chemistry
Kagan Publishing • 1 (800) 933-2667 • www.KaganOnline.com

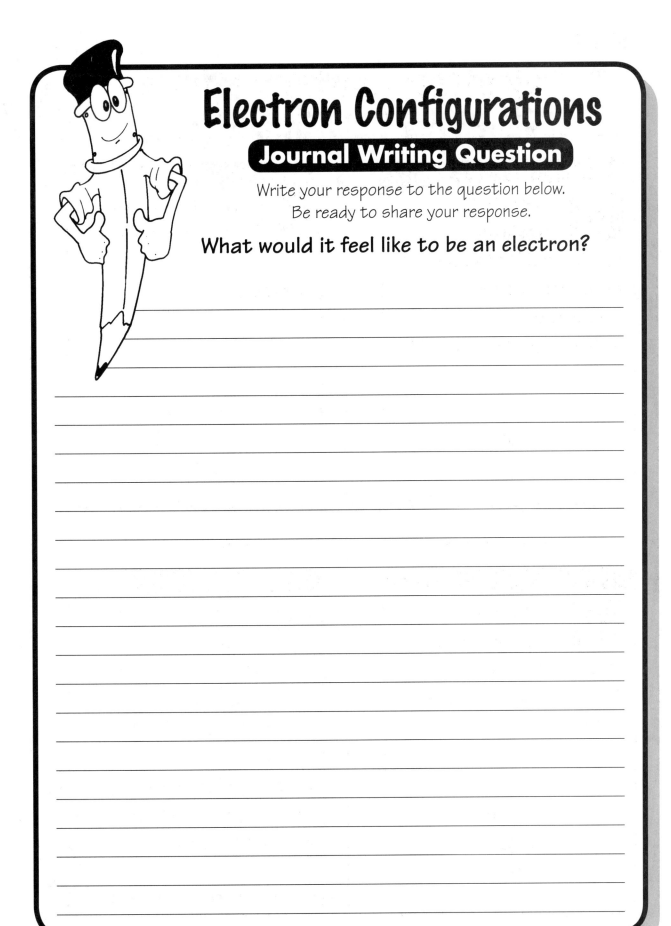

Electron Configurations
Journal Writing Question

Write your response to the question below.
Be ready to share your response.

What would it feel like to be an electron?

Electron Configurations

Question Starters

Use the question starters below to create complete questions.
Send your questions to a partner or to another team to answer.

1. If you were an electron

2. How is an electron an example of

3. How could you improve electron

4. What are some possible ways Lewis Dot structures

5. How could alkali earth metals

6. What would happen if electrons

7. Should orbitals

8. What part of a "p" orbital might

Higher-Level Thinking Questions for Chemistry
Kagan Publishing • 1 (800) 933-2667 • www.KaganOnline.com

Environmental Chemistry and Pollution

The branch of chemistry that studies the conditions of the Earth and the impact of humans on the planet.

higher-level thinking questions

"Be less curious about people and more curious about ideas."

— Marie Curie

Environmental Chemistry and Pollution
Question Cards

Environmental Chemistry and Pollution

1 Pick a type of pollution. What could you propose to reduce/eliminate it at the local and worldwide levels?

Environmental Chemistry and Pollution

2 How are the different layers of the atmosphere affected by air pollution?

Environmental Chemistry and Pollution

3 How can you explain the importance of the ozone layer?

Environmental Chemistry and Pollution

4 In your own words, what are chlorofluorocarbons (CFCs) and what *do* they do?

Environmental Chemistry and Pollution
Question Cards

Environmental Chemistry and Pollution

5 Predict what historical impact acid rain may have for future generations.

Environmental Chemistry and Pollution

6 How do you think smog has affected life in and around cities?

Environmental Chemistry and Pollution

7 How could you use salt water for a lucrative purpose? Explain the chemistry behind your proposal.

Environmental Chemistry and Pollution

8 How have greenhouse gases impacted the global economy over time?

Higher-Level Thinking Questions for Chemistry
Kagan Publishing • 1 (800) 933-2667 • www.KaganOnline.com

Environmental Chemistry and Pollution
Question Cards

Environmental Chemistry and Pollution

9 Should municipal water be fluoridated? Why or why not?

Environmental Chemistry and Pollution

10 What changes in modern society have impacted the use of resources? How have they impacted the environment?

Environmental Chemistry and Pollution

11 A historical site in your town has been marked by the government as chemically polluted. As mayor, what remediation plan would you present to the public at your next town council meeting?

Environmental Chemistry and Pollution

12 What are some of the pros and cons of choosing to "go green" with regard to environmental impact?

Environmental Chemistry and Pollution
Question Cards

13 In your life, how could you apply your knowledge of pollutants as they move through a food chain?

14 How could you express in a drawing, poem, or song the importance of preventing pollution in the environment?

15 Besides fossil fuels, identify several other energy sources that could be used to make fuel. Evaluate which source you feel is best.

16 Describe the pros and cons of using alternative energy sources in your home.

Environmental Chemistry and Pollution

Journal Writing Question

Write your response to the question below.
Be ready to share your response.

How would you feel if you lived in a town where the water supply was polluted with a heavy metal?

_____

_____

_____

_____

_____

_____

_____

_____

_____

_____

_____

_____

_____

_____

_____

_____

_____

Environmental Chemistry and Pollution

Question Starters

Use the question starters below to create complete questions.
Send your questions to a partner or to another team to answer.

1. What is more important

2. What preparations would you

3. How has your thinking changed about

4. How would you approach the problem of

5. What questions do you have about

6. Do you agree with....Why?

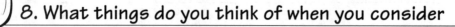

7. What would happen if pollution

8. What things do you think of when you consider

Higher-Level Thinking Questions for Chemistry
Kagan Publishing • 1 (800) 933-2667 • www.KaganOnline.com

Gases

The study of molecules found in the gaseous state, along with the factors that impact their chemical nature.

higher-level thinking questions

"Energy and persistence conquer all things."

— Benjamin Franklin

Higher-Level Thinking Questions for Chemistry
Kagan Publishing • 1 (800) 933-2667 • www.KaganOnline.com

Gases
Question Cards

1 What are some practical applications of a barometer?

2 What might life be like on the earth if atmospheric pressure were not 760 mmHg, but instead greater or less?

3 What are some possible ways to show how the pressure and volume of a gas are inversely proportional?

4 How can you explain why the equation, $PV = nRT$, is significant when studying gases?

Gases
Question Cards

Gases

5 What patterns can you find between Charles's and Boyle's laws?

Gases

6 In your opinion, which of the following gases is most important in our atmosphere: nitrogen, oxygen, argon, or carbon dioxide? Why?

Gases

7 Even though carbon dioxide is a very small portion of air, what impact do you think an increase of CO_2 will have on the Earth?

Gases

8 What is the relationship between the molar mass and particle speed of a gas?

Higher-Level Thinking Questions for Chemistry
Kagan Publishing • 1 (800) 933-2667 • www.KaganOnline.com

Gases
Question Cards

Gases

9 How can you design an experiment to determine how temperature can affect the gas volume in a balloon?

Gases

10 How can gas pressure affect the health of someone who goes scuba diving?

Gases

11 How does an understanding of gases and pressure apply to the field of meteorology?

Gases

12 What would happen to the molecules in a perfume bottle if the bottle fell on the floor and broke open?

Gases
Question Cards

Gases

13 If you had asthma, why would living in an area surrounding the Dead Sea be beneficial to your health? (Remember to think about gas and pressure.)

Gases

14 What would you predict would happen to a soda can with heated water inside of it, if the can were placed in a bowl of ice water? Explain why.

Gases

15 What kind of experiment could show that different gases have different densities?

Gases

16 In what ways could you change your daily life to help reduce air pollution?

Higher-Level Thinking Questions for Chemistry
Kagan Publishing • 1 (800) 933-2667 • www.KaganOnline.com

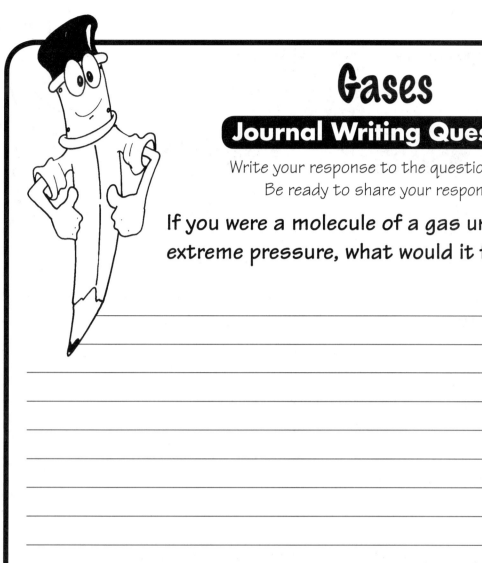

Gases

Journal Writing Question

Write your response to the question below.
Be ready to share your response.

If you were a molecule of a gas under extreme pressure, what would it feel like?

Gases

Question Starters

Use the question starters below to create complete questions.
Send your questions to a partner or to another team to answer.

1. If pressure

2. Should we regulate

3. What impact might air pollution

4. How would you plan to

5. In one sentence, how could Boyle's law

6. What similarities

7. Do you think it is possible for oxygen gas

8. In your life, how could you apply

Higher-Level Thinking Questions for Chemistry
Kagan Publishing • 1 (800) 933-2667 • www.KaganOnline.com

Hydrocarbons and Petroleum

The chemical chains consisting of carbon and hydrogen molecules.

higher-level thinking questions

"Everyday do something that will inch you closer to a better tomorrow."

— Doug Firebaugh

Higher-Level Thinking Questions for Chemistry
Kagan Publishing • 1 (800) 933-2667 • www.KaganOnline.com

Hydrocarbons and Petroleum
Question Cards

Hydrocarbons and Petroleum

1 How can you explain the common features of all hydrocarbons?

Hydrocarbons and Petroleum

2 What patterns can you find in the molecular formula of alkanes as carbons are added?

Hydrocarbons and Petroleum

3 What general rule could be applied to all alcohols?

Hydrocarbons and Petroleum

4 How are aldehydes related to ketones?

Hydrocarbons and Petroleum
Question Cards

Hydrocarbons and Petroleum

5 What are some practical uses of alcohols in your daily life?

Hydrocarbons and Petroleum

6 What might your life be like without petroleum-based products?

Hydrocarbons and Petroleum

7 Do you think the hydrophobic properties of petroleum products makes for a more or less difficult cleanup of oil spills? Explain.

Hydrocarbons and Petroleum

8 Why is the flammable nature of many hydrocarbons so important to humans?

Higher-Level Thinking Questions for Chemistry
Kagan Publishing • 1 (800) 933-2667 • www.KaganOnline.com

Hydrocarbons and Petroleum
Question Cards

Hydrocarbons and Petroleum

9 How does the chemical structure of alkanes, alkenes, and alkynes relate to their reactivity?

Hydrocarbons and Petroleum

10 Compare and contrast the United States and the Middle East with regard to population, petroleum reserves, and petroleum consumption. What are the consequences of these factors?

Hydrocarbons and Petroleum

11 Propose a generalization between the number of carbon atoms in a hydrocarbon molecule and its viscosity.

Hydrocarbons and Petroleum

12 How does the density of oil impact the environment during an oil fire?

Hydrocarbons and Petroleum
Question Cards

Hydrocarbons and Petroleum

13 In what ways has the use of petroleum changed over time in our society? Compare three generations: you, your parents, and your grandparents.

Hydrocarbons and Petroleum

14 What is the relationship between viscosity and temperature?

Hydrocarbons and Petroleum

15 Why is the hydrocarbon industry so important in today's world?

Hydrocarbons and Petroleum

16 Compare and contrast the characteristics of a saturated and an unsaturated hydrocarbon molecule.

Higher-Level Thinking Questions for Chemistry
Kagan Publishing • 1 (800) 933-2667 • www.KaganOnline.com

Hydrocarbons and Petroleum

Journal Writing Question

Write your response to the question below.
Be ready to share your response.

Predict what our lives will be like in twenty-five years in relation to petroleum and fuel use.

_____

_____

_____

_____

_____

_____

_____

_____

_____

_____

_____

_____

_____

_____

_____

_____

_____

_____

_____

_____

Hydrocarbons and Petroleum
Question Starters

Use the question starters below to create complete questions.
Send your questions to a partner or to another team to answer.

1. How could oil

2. Do you think it is possible for alcohols

3. What role

4. What impact might fossil fuels have

5. How is a ketone related to a

6. In your own words, what is

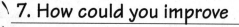 7. How could you improve

8. What is another way oil can

Higher-Level Thinking Questions for Chemistry
Kagan Publishing • 1 (800) 933-2667 • www.KaganOnline.com

Metals

The majority of the elements in the periodic table are metals that exhibit the properties of luster, malleability, conductivity, and ductility.

higher-level thinking questions

"We are what we repeatedly do. Excellence, therefore, is not an act, but a habit."

— Aristotle

Higher-Level Thinking Questions for Chemistry
Kagan Publishing • 1 (800) 933-2667 • www.KaganOnline.com

Metals
Question Cards

Metals

1 What are the differences between metals and nonmetals?

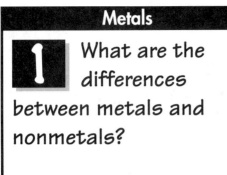

Metals

2 How can you explain the role of metals in a battery?

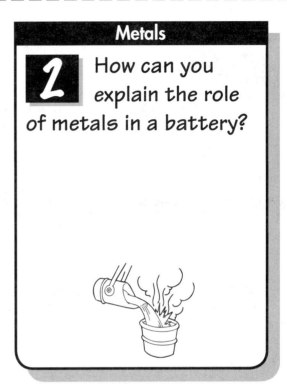

Metals

3 What metals impact your daily life? Explain how.

Metals

4 How is gold jewelry an example of an alloy?

Metals
Question Cards

Metals

5 What could you invent to streamline the process of mining for precious metals?

Metals

6 What reasons might explain the color of the Statue of Liberty?

Metals

7 What steps are involved in the smelting of a metal?

Metals

8 What would the world be like without magnets?

Higher-Level Thinking Questions for Chemistry
Kagan Publishing • 1 (800) 933-2667 • www.KaganOnline.com

Metals
Question Cards

Metals

9 You are an artist who has been hired to create a statue for your school. What would you sculpt? What metal would you choose to work with and why?

Metals

10 In what ways does an understanding of heavy metals impact your life?

Metals

11 Explain why different coins might melt at different rates.

Metals

12 Predict how you think recycling may impact the future use of metals as a resource in your community, state, country, and the world at large.

Metals
Question Cards

13 You are mining during the Gold Rush and come across a gold substance. How could you determine if it is pyrite (fool's gold) or gold (Au)?

14 How is the process of electrochemistry important to the chemical industry? In what ways does it impact your life?

15 An electro-chemical plant is looking into build-ing in your town. What are three benefits and three drawbacks of this plan for your town?

16 A company is trying to determine which of two future mining sites to invest in. What are five factors they should consider that will make the most profit for the company?

Higher-Level Thinking Questions for Chemistry
Kagan Publishing • 1 (800) 933-2667 • www.KaganOnline.com

Metals

Journal Writing Question

Write your response to the question below.
Be ready to share your response.

Car frames used to be made from steel with chrome bumpers. Today they are made from aluminum, fiberglass, and plastics. Discuss three different reasons why you think the automobile manufacturers made these changes.

_____

_____

_____

_____

_____

_____

_____

_____

_____

_____

_____

_____

_____

_____

_____

_____

Metals

Question Starters

Use the question starters below to create complete questions.
Send your questions to a partner or to another team to answer.

1. If you were a magnet

2. In your own words, how can metalloids

3. How can alloys

4. What practical applications to heating

5. How could you get rid of

6. How could you test if a metal

7. What general rule about transition metals

8. What qualities of steel

Higher-Level Thinking Questions for Chemistry
Kagan Publishing • 1 (800) 933-2667 • www.KaganOnline.com

Methods and Tools

The tools and techniques used in the field of chemistry to conduct scientific experiments.

higher-level thinking questions

"They can because they think they can."

— Virgil

Higher-Level Thinking Questions for Chemistry
Kagan Publishing • 1 (800) 933-2667 • www.KaganOnline.com

Methods and Tools
Question Cards

1 How could a titration be used in everyday life?

2 How could you compare the different methods of measuring volume?

3 What could you invent to improve measurement in a chemistry lab?

4 In your own words, explain the differences between precision and accuracy.

Methods and Tools
Question Cards

5 Describe the procedure used to mass an object using a triple beam balance and an electronic balance. Which do you prefer and why?

6 How would you sequence the steps involved in solving a problem when asked to convert units?

7 How could you act out or describe the proper way to clean up a chemical spill?

8 What kinds of measurements have you performed today?

Methods and Tools
Question Cards

Methods and Tools

9 What reasons do scientists have for using significant digits in the laboratory?

Methods and Tools

10 By what criteria would you assess the scientific validity of a set of data?

Methods and Tools

11 What are the differences between qualitative and quantitative data?

Methods and Tools

12 How could you summarize the steps involved in conducting an accurate chemical measurement?

Methods and Tools
Question Cards

Methods and Tools

13 What are some common causes of error in the laboratory setting?

Methods and Tools

14 If all electronic devices were removed from your lab, how would you go about performing your experiment and collecting data?

Methods and Tools

15 If you could ask a question of any inventor of a scientific tool used in our lab, what would you ask them and why?

Methods and Tools

16 How is the scientific method similar to a chef designing a new recipe?

Methods and Tools

Journal Writing Question

Write your response to the question below.
Be ready to share your response.

How could you use your knowledge of scientific tools and methods in your everyday life?

_____

_____

_____

_____

_____

_____

_____

_____

_____

_____

_____

_____

_____

_____

_____

_____

_____

_____

Methods and Tools
Question Starters

Use the question starters below to create complete questions.
Send your questions to a partner or to another team to answer.

1. If you were a scientist

2. How would you approach

3. What kind of tool could

4. If you had to design a lab

5. How does the scientific method

6. How could you find out more

 7. What observations can

8. How could you use

Higher-Level Thinking Questions for Chemistry
Kagan Publishing • 1 (800) 933-2667 • www.KaganOnline.com

Nuclear Chemistry and Alternative Energy Sources

The study of nuclear reactions and nontraditional energy sources.

higher-level thinking questions

"A person who never made a mistake never tried anything new."

— Albert Einstein

Nuclear Chemistry and Alternative Energy Sources
Question Cards

Nuclear Chemistry and Alternative Energy Sources

1 What changes occur in an element during radioactive decay?

Nuclear Chemistry and Alternative Energy Sources

2 Compare alpha and beta emissions to each other. What are the similarities and differences between them?

Nuclear Chemistry and Alternative Energy Sources

3 How could you sequence the decay of uranium-238 to lead-206?

Nuclear Chemistry and Alternative Energy Sources

4 What is the significance of a particle accelerator?

Nuclear Chemistry and Alternative Energy Sources
Question Cards

Nuclear Chemistry and Alternative Energy Sources

5 If you could invent any machine for use on radioactive waste, what would it be and how would it work?

Nuclear Chemistry and Alternative Energy Sources

6 How could you explain what a half-life is to an elementary school student?

Nuclear Chemistry and Alternative Energy Sources

7 What is C-14 dating and how is it significant to the study of life?

Nuclear Chemistry and Alternative Energy Sources

8 In your opinion, which radioactive dating technique is most important? Why?

Higher-Level Thinking Questions for Chemistry
Kagan Publishing • 1 (800) 933-2667 • www.KaganOnline.com

Nuclear Chemistry and Alternative Energy Sources
Question Cards

Nuclear Chemistry and Alternative Energy Sources

9 In what order would you rank nuclear, wind, and solar energy? Why?

Nuclear Chemistry and Alternative Energy Sources

10 What are some of the pros and cons of using nuclear energy?

Nuclear Chemistry and Alternative Energy Sources

11 Distinguish between ionizing and non-ionizing radiation.

Nuclear Chemistry and Alternative Energy Sources

12 Chemically speaking, why is radiating a living cell potentially detrimental?

Nuclear Chemistry and Alternative Energy Sources
Question Cards

Nuclear Chemistry and Alternative Energy Sources

13 What is your opinion about the use of nuclear power plants near your home?

Nuclear Chemistry and Alternative Energy Sources

14 Compare and contrast the similarities and differences between nuclear fission and nuclear fusion.

Nuclear Chemistry and Alternative Energy Sources

15 If you could interview Albert Einstein, what five questions would you ask him?

Nuclear Chemistry and Alternative Energy Sources

16 A wind farm has been proposed in your area. What are some of the potential benefits and drawbacks of this energy source?

Higher-Level Thinking Questions for Chemistry
Kagan Publishing • 1 (800) 933-2667 • www.KaganOnline.com

Nuclear Chemistry and Alternative Energy Sources

Journal Writing Question

Write your response to the question below.
Be ready to share your response.

You are lobbying in support of a bill that would utilize an alternative energy source to power your school. What ideas would you include in your position statement to gain support?

_____

_____

_____

_____

_____

_____

_____

_____

_____

_____

_____

_____

_____

_____

_____

_____

_____

Nuclear Chemistry and
Alternative Energy Sources

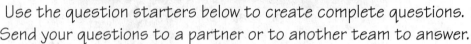

Question Starters

Use the question starters below to create complete questions.
Send your questions to a partner or to another team to answer.

1. If you were a C-14 molecule

2. Do you think it is possible for radioactive uranium to

3. Should radioactive waste

4. How might alternative energy sources

5. What do you think would happen if solar energy

6. In one sentence, how could fission

7. Should a nuclear power plant

8. How has Chernobyl

Higher-Level Thinking Questions for Chemistry
Kagan Publishing • 1 (800) 933-2667 • www.KaganOnline.com

Periodic Table

A table that arranges the chemical elements, based on atomic number and periodic law.

higher-level thinking questions

"If you're going to be thinking anyway, you might as well think big."

— Donald Trump

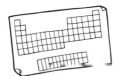

Periodic Table
Question Cards

1 Choose one of the following elements: hydrogen, oxygen, carbon, or chlorine. Answer the following: If you were that element, what element would you most like to combine with? Why?

2 Discuss why today's human population and technology have put huge strains on the Earth's chemical resources.

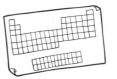

3 List any three elements that are in the same family. What do these elements have in common? List at least three items.

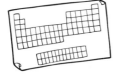

4 Compare and contrast the physical and chemical properties of metals, metalloids, and nonmetals.

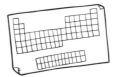

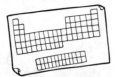

Periodic Table
Question Cards

Periodic Table

5 Use your body to act out what you think would happen if you hit a sample of each of the following elements with a hammer: nickel, phosphorous, iodine, and zirconium.

Periodic Table

6 Pretend you are a scientist at the time of the Hindenberg explosion. How would you explain that using helium gas would have been safer than using hydrogen gas?

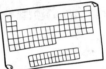

Periodic Table

7 How would you feel if you were one of the electrons found in the outer orbital of a nonmetal element of the periodic table?

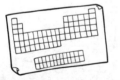

Periodic Table

8 If you could create a new element, what would you name it and what would its properties be?

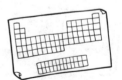

Higher-Level Thinking Questions for Chemistry
Kagan Publishing • 1 (800) 933-2667 • www.KaganOnline.com

Periodic Table
Question Cards

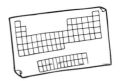

Periodic Table

9 What is your favorite characteristic of the periodic table? Why?

Periodic Table

10 How could you explain why the noble gases are all grouped together?

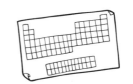

Periodic Table

11 In your own words, what is the significance of the arrangement of columns of the periodic table?

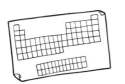

Periodic Table

12 How is sodium related to potassium?

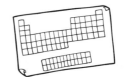

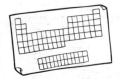

Periodic Table
Question Cards

Periodic Table

13 What is another way you could arrange the elements instead of using the periodic table?

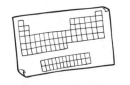

Periodic Table

14 If you were going to guess, why are the lanthanides and actinides in their own section at the bottom of the periodic table?

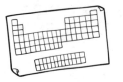

Periodic Table

15 What qualities of the alkali metals make them so interesting?

Periodic Table

16 Predict where a newly discovered element with six valence electrons would be placed on the periodic table. Why?

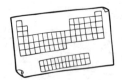

Higher-Level Thinking Questions for Chemistry
Kagan Publishing • 1 (800) 933-2667 • www.KaganOnline.com

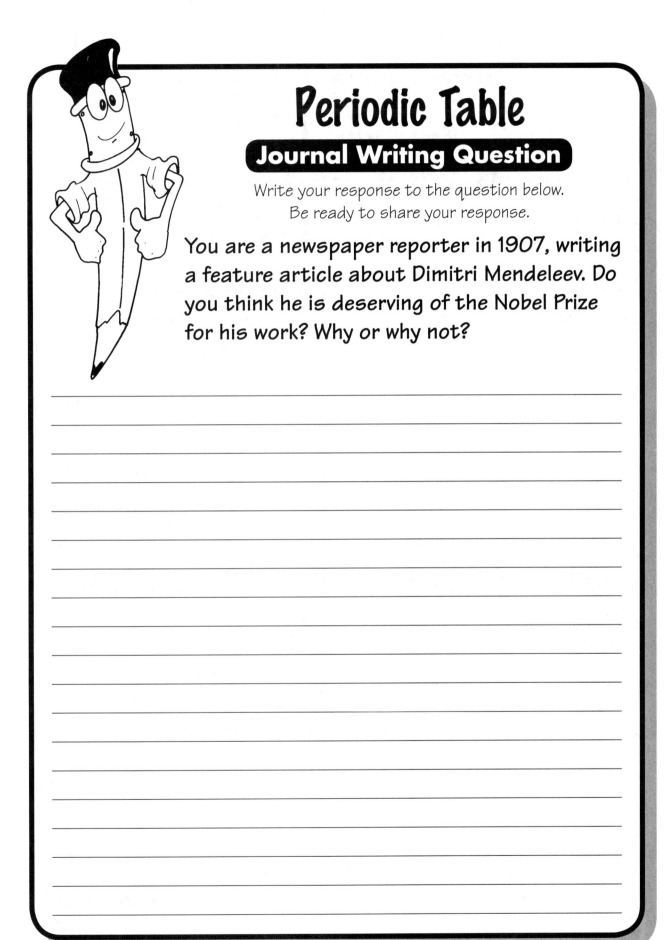

Periodic Table

Journal Writing Question

Write your response to the question below.
Be ready to share your response.

You are a newspaper reporter in 1907, writing a feature article about Dimitri Mendeleev. Do you think he is deserving of the Nobel Prize for his work? Why or why not?

Periodic Table
Question Starters

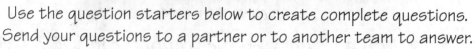

Use the question starters below to create complete questions.
Send your questions to a partner or to another team to answer.

1. How can the periodic table be used to

2. Using any element, what experiment could

you do to

3. What role does arrangement of the periodic table have on

4. Why can hydrogen

5. If you were an element

6. Do you think it is possible for noble gases

7. What impact might chlorine

8. What do you think would happen if gold

Higher-Level Thinking Questions for Chemistry
Kagan Publishing • 1 (800) 933-2667 • www.KaganOnline.com

Solutions

Homogeneous mixtures of two or more substances.

higher-level thinking questions

"You must look into other people as well as at them."

—Lord Chesterfield

Solutions
Question Cards

1 What characteristics do all solutions have?

2 How is coffee an example of a solution?

3 What impact does solubility have on your daily life?

4 What is the relationship between a solvent and a solute?

Solutions
Question Cards

5 How could you explain why solubility varies depending on temperature?

6 In your own words, how would you explain equilibrium? Provide a real world example.

7 What experiment could you design to test the solubility of salt in water?

8 How does melting ice on a roadway relate to freezing-point depression?

Higher-Level Thinking Questions for Chemistry
Kagan Publishing • 1 (800) 933-2667 • www.KaganOnline.com

Solutions
Question Cards

Solutions

9 What are the predicted effects of temperature and pressure on the solubility of a solute? How would these effects differ for the solubility of gases in water?

Solutions

10 Give an example of an aqueous solution. Describe which item is the solvent and which is the solute.

Solutions

11 What are some possible ways to test the concentration of a solute within a solution?

Solutions

12 How does solubility depend on environmental conditions?

Solutions
Question Cards

13 What is the relationship between a solubility curve and the placement of an element within the periodic table?

14 In your own words, define the following expression: "Like dissolves like."

15 You are trying to make a gelatin solution. What could you do to increase the speed of the reaction?

16 Predict what would happen to a carbonated drink if it were left open in the hot sun. Why?

Higher-Level Thinking Questions for Chemistry
Kagan Publishing • 1 (800) 933-2667 • www.KaganOnline.com

Solutions

Journal Writing Question

Write your response to the question below.
Be ready to share your response.

Think of three things in your home that are solutions. Why are they categorized as solutions?

Solutions

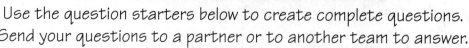

Use the question starters below to create complete questions.
Send your questions to a partner or to another team to answer.

1. What impact might boiling-point elevation

_____

2. How could you get rid of

_____

3. What role does salt play

_____

4. How does sugar

_____

5. How would you plan to

_____

6. What did you notice about

_____

7. What machine could

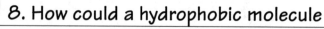

8. How could a hydrophobic molecule

_____

Higher-Level Thinking Questions for Chemistry
Kagan Publishing • 1 (800) 933-2667 • www.KaganOnline.com

States of Matter

Matter can be found in three different states: solid, liquid, and gas.

higher-level thinking questions

"I light my candle from their torches."

— Robert Burton

Higher-Level Thinking Questions for Chemistry
Kagan Publishing • 1 (800) 933-2667 • www.KaganOnline.com

States of Matter

1 What would it feel like if you were a water molecule going from ice to water, and then to steam?

States of Matter

2 In your own words, what are "van der Waals forces"?

States of Matter

3 How can you explain why ice floats?

States of Matter

4 In a sentence, how would you describe viscosity?

States of Matter
Question Cards

States of Matter

5 How can you represent a "phase diagram" in words?

States of Matter

6 What is the significance of the triple point?

States of Matter

7 How could you explain why sublimation occurs?

States of Matter

8 What is an example of a machine in your life that exhibits all three states of matter? Explain.

Higher-Level Thinking Questions for Chemistry
Kagan Publishing • 1 (800) 933-2667 • www.KaganOnline.com

States of Matter
Question Cards

States of Matter

9 Why would water be used on citrus trees when the overnight temperature is expected to drop below freezing?

States of Matter

10 Why does maple sugar flow from a tree in the winter?

States of Matter

11 Explain the relationship between water's molecular configuration in the three states of matter and their physical characteristics.

States of Matter

12 What would the movement of water's molecules be like if it were a solid? Liquid? Gas? Use your body to act it out.

States of Matter

13 Using pictures, describe what happens to the physical arrangement of molecules as they move from liquid to gas and from liquid to solid.

States of Matter

14 What are the similarities and differences between sublimation and desposition? Describe using both words and pictures.

States of Matter

15 Compare and contrast the energy exchanges that occur during an exothermic and an endothermic chemical reaction.

States of Matter

16 What effect does surface tension have on living organisms?

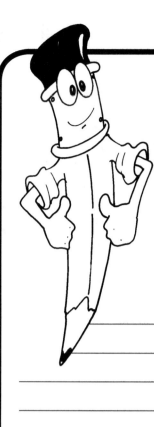

States of Matter

Journal Writing Question

Write your response to the question below.
Be ready to share your response.

Which state of matter reminds you most of your personality? Explain why.

_____

_____

_____

_____

_____

_____

_____

_____

_____

_____

_____

_____

_____

_____

_____

_____

_____

_____

_____

_____

States of Matter
Question Starters

Use the question starters below to create complete questions.
Send your questions to a partner or to another team to answer.

1. If you were a water molecule about to boil

2. Do you think a gas could

3. How can ice

4. What do you think would happen if all liquids

5. What is your opinion about

6. How could you break down

7. How would you compare the states of matter to

8. What is another way condensation

Higher-Level Thinking Questions for Chemistry
Kagan Publishing • 1 (800) 933-2667 • www.KaganOnline.com

Stoichiometry

The measurement of elements based upon the law of conservation of mass.

higher-level thinking questions

"Success is the sum of small efforts, repeated day in and day out."

— Robert Collier

Higher-Level Thinking Questions for Chemistry
Kagan Publishing • 1 (800) 933-2667 • www.KaganOnline.com

Stoichiometry
Question Cards

1 How could you explain the concept of a mole to a child?

2 What questions do you having regarding stoichiometry?

3 What connections can you make between equation writing and solving algebraic equations?

4 In your own words, what is factor labeling?

Stoichiometry
Question Cards

5 In your mind, what is the most significant thing to consider when balancing an equation?

6 How could you summarize the relationship between grams and moles?

7 If you were going to guess, how much space would a mole of gold molecules take up?

8 Sequence the steps involved in solving a molar mass conversion problem.

Higher-Level Thinking Questions for Chemistry
Kagan Publishing • 1 (800) 933-2667 • www.KaganOnline.com

Stoichiometry
Question Cards

Stoichiometry

9 Sequence the steps involved in balancing this chemical equation: "the decomposition of hydrogen peroxide into water and oxygen;" then write the balanced equation using chemical symbols.

Stoichiometry

10 How could you summarize the process of using the factor label method during the collection of laboratory data?

Stoichiometry

11 What analogy can you invent to explain how or why moles are used in chemistry?

Stoichiometry

12 How is a chemical equation similar to a before-and-after picture?

Stoichiometry
Question Cards

Stoichiometry

13 Describe in words how to make your favorite food. Write it out in the form of a chemical equation.

Stoichiometry

14 What is common to solving all molar mass problems?

Stoichiometry

15 Would you prefer to balance an equation moving forward or backward? Why?

Stoichiometry

16 Do you think the advancement of chemistry would have changed if Antoine Lavoisier had not been executed? Explain.

Higher-Level Thinking Questions for Chemistry
Kagan Publishing • 1 (800) 933-2667 • www.KaganOnline.com

Stoichiometry

Journal Writing Question

Write your response to the question below.
Be ready to share your response.

How could you use your knowledge of conversions and balancing in your everyday life?

_____
_____
_____
_____
_____
_____
_____
_____
_____
_____
_____
_____
_____
_____
_____
_____
_____
_____

Stoichiometry
Question Starters

Use the question starters below to create complete questions.
Send your questions to a partner or to another team to answer.

1. What would happen if a mole

_____

2. How can Avogadro's number

_____

3. What purpose do equations

_____

4. How could you simplify

_____

5. If you were Amedeo Avogadro, what

_____

6. How do coefficients

_____

7. How does the rearrangement of

_____

8. What is the significance of

_____

Higher-Level Thinking Questions for Chemistry
Kagan Publishing • 1 (800) 933-2667 • www.KaganOnline.com

Water

A molecule with two hydrogen atoms covalently bonded to an oxygen atom; the Earth's most essential molecule.

higher-level thinking questions

"Fortune favors the prepared mind."

— Louis Pasteur

Higher-Level Thinking Questions for Chemistry
Kagan Publishing • 1 (800) 933-2667 • www.KaganOnline.com

Water
Question Cards

Water
Question Cards

Water

5 If you could create a new property of water, what would it be and why?

Water

6 How would you describe the organization of water as a liquid?

Water

7 What role do hydroxide and hydronium ions play in liquid water?

Water

8 In what ways does water's polarity impact your daily life?

Higher-Level Thinking Questions for Chemistry
Kagan Publishing • 1 (800) 933-2667 • www.KaganOnline.com

Water
Question Cards

Water

9 If you were responsible for devising a water conservation plan in your town, how would you prioritize your actions?

Water

10 What would happen to life on Earth if ice didn't float?

Water

11 What connections can you make between water's atomic structure and its physical properties?

Water

12 What experiment could you design to purify a water sample?

Water
Question Cards

13 What are the consequences for an aquatic eco-system that has been contaminated with a pollutant?

14 In what ways have you used water today?

15 How do you think the daily use of water differs around the world? What connections can you make to your life?

16 What are the advantages and disadvantages of making "pure water" accessible to all?

Water

Journal Writing Question

Write your response to the question below.
Be ready to share your response.

How would you begin to approach the problem of isolating and determining the source of pollution in a body of water near your school?

_____

_____

_____

_____

_____

_____

_____

_____

_____

_____

_____

_____

_____

_____

_____

_____

Water

Question Starters

Use the question starters below to create complete questions.
Send your questions to a partner or to another team to answer.

1. What if water did not

_____

_____

2. What qualities of water

_____

_____

3. How can hydrogen bonds

_____

_____

4. Do you think it is possible for water to

_____

_____

5. How does humidity

_____

_____

6. What connections can weather have with

_____

_____

7. What significance does cohesion

_____

_____

8. If you were a meteorologist

_____

Higher-Level Thinking Questions for Chemistry
Kagan Publishing • 1 (800) 933-2667 • www.KaganOnline.com

Notes